MARCHING OFF THE MAP
Interactive Travel Guide

TIM ELMORE
with ANDREW McPEAK

Poet Gardener
PUBLISHING

Published in Atlanta, Georgia, by Poet Gardener Publishing in association with Growing Leaders, Inc.
www.GrowingLeaders.com

ISBN: 978-0-9966970-7-1
Printed in the United States of America

Library of Congress Cataloguing-in-Publication Data

MARCHING OFF THE MAP

INSPIRE STUDENTS TO NAVIGATE A BRAND NEW WORLD

INTERACTIVE
TRAVEL GUIDE

TIM ELMORE
with ANDREW McPEAK

HOW TO USE THIS GUIDE
A LETTER FROM DR. TIM ELMORE

Since 1979, I have worked with the next generation, leading them to become young men and women who solve the world's problems and serve those less fortunate than themselves. The trouble is, I've seen more change in our world in the last 10 years than in all of my prior work. No doubt you have seen this change too.

This Travel Guide is designed to help you navigate our changing landscape. While, I am sure you are already an engaged leader, teacher, coach, or manager, even the best leaders can get left behind if the world moves forward and they stay put. Leadership, especially leadership of our young, requires us to be people who are both timely (in touch with the present needs and problems of today's world) and timeless (understanding of the never changing foundations upon which leadership is built). Being this type of leader takes commitment, reflection, and practice. That's what this travel guide is designed to help you do.

As you read *Marching Off the Map*, you'll no doubt think of many ideas for new directions you could take. I hope you'll be challenged to rethink the best ways to lead youth today. If you're challenged but never take action, or are presented with new ideas and are never asked to reflect on it, change is not likely to occur. This guide was created to give you a place to write down your ideas, ask yourself big questions, and contextualize the content of the book to your work.

As you finish each chapter in *Marching Off the Map*, return to this travel guide to reflect. I encourage you to write in the margins, come up with new ideas, and share them with your colleagues. Fill up this now unused guide so it can become a roadmap for your work. No one knows your context quite like you, so use this as a roadmap on the path to better leadership.

Thanks for what you do,

Dr. Tim Elmore
Founder and President of Growing Leaders

CONTENTS

PART THREE: How Must We Change?

Chapter 1
WHAT IF THE FUTURE COULD TALK TO US?

We may need to change.

- TIM ELMORE

EXERCISE: LET'S GO BACK IN TIME. LIST THREE THINGS THAT
HAVE CHANGED SINCE YOU WERE A CHILD:

1. _Morning cartoons_____

2. _____

3. _____

4. _____

EXERCISE: IN A WORLD OF INNOVATION OVER TRADITION AND
REASON, NAME FIVE THINGS YOUR STUDENTS ARE BETTER AT
THAN YOU:

1. _Keeping up with their social media presence_____

2. _____

3. _____

4. _____

5. _____

QUESTION: THERE ARE MANY THINGS YOUR STUDENTS ARE BETTER AT THAN YOU. HOW DOES THIS REALITY CHANGE THE TEACHER-STUDENT RELATIONSHIP FROM HOW IT MIGHT HAVE BEEN 30 YEARS AGO?

_____

_____

_____

_____

QUESTION: THERE'S A NEW REALITY IN OUR WORLD TODAY THAT I SPOKE ABOUT IN *WHAT IF THE FUTURE COULD TALK TO US?*, "THE EXTINCTION OF CHILDLIKENESS," AND "THE EXTENSION OF CHILDISHNESS." HOW HAVE YOU SEEN THIS TO BE TRUE IN THE STUDENTS YOU WORK WITH TODAY?

_____

_____

_____

_____

Chapter 2
HOW DO YOU MARCH OFF A MAP?

Life is not neat; it is messy. And the sooner I embrace that, the better off I will be.

- TIM ELMORE

QUESTION: REACT TO THE QUOTE ABOVE. IS THIS TRUE? HOW HAVE YOU EMBRACED THE 'MESSINESS' OF LIFE IN THE CLASSROOM OR IN YOUR LEADERSHIP OF THE NEXT GENERATION?

_____

_____

_____

_____

QUESTION: DO YOU NATURALLY LEAN TOWARD "RISK" OR "ROUTINE?" (P. 19, *MARCHING OFF THE MAP*)

RISK   ROUTINE

◄───►

QUESTION: THINK ABOUT ALEXANDER THE GREAT. HE CONSCRIPTED MEN INTO HIS ARMY TO BECOME MAP MAKERS, RECORDING THE PATH AS THEY WENT. WHO ARE ONE OR TWO "ALEXANDER THE GREATS" IN YOUR LIFE? WHO ARE THE TEACHERS WHO HELPED YOU SEE A NEW PATH, TRY A NEW METHOD, OR CHANGE YOUR VIEW OF YOUR PROFESSION?

_____

_____

_____

_____

WHY WE FEAR THE UNKNOWN

Like the ancient map makers, sometimes we make monsters out of the unknown.

1. "NEW" MEANS NO GUARANTEES.
   How will we know if we are about to fail?

2. THE RULES FOR OUR PROFESSION ARE ALREADY SET.
   There's a good chance the people around you don't want things to change.

3. CHANGE MEANS ACKNOWLEDGING THAT WHAT WE ARE DOING ISN'T WORKING.
   Are we prepared to admit we've been wrong?

4. CHANGE TAKES WORK.
   The solution you need may require extra hours and late nights.

5. IF OUR CHANGE WORKS, PEOPLE WILL LOOK TO US FOR LEADERSHIP.
   If we lead the way to change, others will come to us for help.

EXERCISE: USE YOUR EXPERIENCE AS A LEADER OR TEACHER TO FILL THE CHART COMPARING THE CHARACTERISTICS OF PIONEERS AND SETTLERS IN YOUR PROFESSION.

SETTLERS	PIONEERS
1. Using the same curriculum from 20 years ago	1. Starting off the year by asking students what they want to learn about
2. _____ _____	2. _____ _____
3. _____ _____	3. _____ _____
4. _____ _____	4. _____ _____
5. _____ _____	5. _____ _____

"There are no guarantees of success. But, I can certainly guarantee failure if you remain a settler."

— TIM ELMORE

QUESTION: WHAT ARE SOME MORALS, PRINCIPLES, OR PRACTICES YOU CONSIDER TO BE "TIMELESS?"

_____

_____

_____

_____

MARCHING OFF THE MAP

EXERCISE: DO YOU SEE EXAMPLES OF AN ANTIQUATED SYSTEM WHERE YOU ARE?

List some antiquated practices in your classroom, school, and/ or organization that should probably change: (p. 32, *Marching Off the Map*)

1. _____

2. _____

3. _____

4. _____

5. _____

6. _____

7. _____

8. _____

9. _____

10. _____

QUESTION: IF WE WERE TO START OVER AND CREATE A NEW EDUCATIONAL SYSTEM TODAY, WHAT WOULD WE DIFFERENTLY? WOULD WE LAUNCH NEW METHODS OR SIMPLY REPEAT WHAT WE'VE ALWAYS DONE? (P. 34, *MARCHING OFF THE MAP*)

_____

_____

_____

_____

Chapter 3
WHO ARE TODAY'S NEW NATIVES?

Today's kids need adults to believe in them.

- TIM ELMORE

EXERCISE: A GENERATION Z CHECKLIST. WHICH OF THESE REALITIES HAVE YOU SEEN IN YOUR CLASSROOM OR SCHOOL? (CHECK ALL THAT APPLY.)

☐ Their movies are *Hunger Games* and *Divergent*, where youth are slaughtered and kids no longer feel central to the world.

☐ They multi-task on five screens, not one or two. They experience FOMO: Fear Of Missing Out. They try to consume everything at once.

☐ They have strong filters inside. Teen attention spans have gone from 12 seconds in 2000, to six seconds today. We'd better be engaging them if we want their attention.

☐ They plan to get educated and start working earlier, but they will be "school hackers" and not necessarily attend a traditional liberal arts college.

☐ They tend to feel overwhelmed. They can be full of angst, living in a broken world they never unplug from—receiving 1,000 messages a day.

QUESTION: WHAT OTHER CHARACTERISTICS HAVE YOU OBSERVED? HOW ARE THESE NEW REALITIES AFFECTING YOUR SCHOOL OR CLASSROOM? (P. 45, *MARCHING OFF THE MAP*)

_____

_____

_____

_____

BONUS: THREE PARADOXES FOR GENERATION Z

As you can see, they'll become adults with a different mindset than their older siblings or aunts and uncles. This new day requires a new style of leadership from us. It requires leaders who can help them navigate strange paradoxical realities:

1. Their world will continue to feel bigger as they are growing up in a global economy, but their peer group at home will actually be smaller. They will compete for jobs against the world's best and brightest, yet they'll live in the shadows of a much larger Millennial generation at home. As a smaller population, they may not receive the attention the Millennials got, much like Generation X grew up in the shadows of the Baby Boomers.

2. Thanks to social media, they'll continue to be savvy to information and culture yet may be naïve since the information requires no experience. They'll know so much yet so little, as they can now choose their news feeds and miss a bigger picture. This can produce what I call "artificial maturity," where they're over-exposed to information, yet under-exposed to real-life application.

3. Their world will challenge them to be healthy—physically and emotionally—yet the default is a sedentary lifestyle in front of a screen. Life is on-demand. They can binge on anything that feels good. As leaders, we'll need to help them negotiate between the desires (dreams) they have and the disciplines required to fulfill those desires. And in the midst of this, keep their hope alive for a better future.

QUESTION: LEARNING WHAT YOU HAVE ABOUT THIS GENERATION, SPEND SOME TIME THINKING ABOUT THIS QUESTION: HOW WILL YOU REACH GENERATION Z? (P. 43, *MARCHING OFF THE MAP*)

_____

_____

_____

_____

BONUS: ADDITIONAL QUESTIONS WE CAN ASK AS WE ATTEMPT TO LEAD THEM WELL. (P. 49, *MARCHING OFF THE MAP*)

- How can we help them step out, take risks and show bravery?
- How can we help them see the bright side of things and stay hopeful?
- How can we aid them to sort out goals and find the right educational path?
- How can we affirm the idea of saving money and planning ahead?
- How can we foster their creative gifts and monetize them in their career?
- How can we help them see the power of sending constructive messages?
- How can we utilize metaphors and images to communicate with them?

EXERCISE: HOW WELL DO YOU CONNECT WITH THE NEXT GENERATION? FOR EACH OF THE PRINCIPLES OF CONNECTION BELOW, GIVE YOURSELF A LETTER GRADE (A THROUGH F). REFER TO PAGE 50 IN *MARCHING OFF THE MAP* IF YOU NEED MORE INFORMATION.

TO CONNECT WITH GENERATION Z, WE SHOULD: YOUR GRADE:

    1. Keep it short.   _____

    2. Make it visual.   _____

    3. Feed curiosity.   _____

    4. Give them ownership.   _____

    5. Make it interactive.   _____

    6. Gamify your content.   _____

    7. Offer a cause.   _____

QUESTION: HOW DO YOU PIONEER NEW TERRITORY BY ENGAGING STUDENTS IN REAL PROBLEMS? (P. 53, *MARCHING OFF THE MAP*)

_____

_____

_____

_____

EXERCISE: USE THIS SPACE TO BRAINSTORM AND WRITE DOWN ANY IDEAS YOU'VE THOUGHT OF WHILE READING THIS CHAPTER FOR HOW TO BETTER ENGAGE THE STUDENTS IN YOUR CLASSROOM, SCHOOL, OR ORGANIZATION. (CIRCLE YOUR BEST IDEA!)

Chapter 4
WHAT ARE THE LANDMARKS ON THE NEW MAP?

We will need to help them plan for a future we can only imagine.

- TIM ELMORE

REFLECT AND RESPOND: CONSIDER WHAT HAS HAPPENED IN OUR COUNTRY SINCE THE YEAR 2000.

- We entered a new century and millennium.
- We experienced the largest terrorist attack on our soil.
- We began hearing of corporate scandals: Enron, Tyco, Worldcom, etc.
- The economy began to shift downward, in both business and real estate.
- Trust in government waned measurably after two presidential scandals.
- A war in the Persian Gulf began and has continued their entire lives.
- TSA and the Department of Homeland Security nudged us to focus on safety.

How do you think these factors have affected the students in your school or classroom? How can you leverage these realities to equip the young for life? (p. 66, *Marching Off the Map*)

_____

_____

_____

_____

MARCHING OFF THE MAP

QUESTION: REACHING THIS GENERATION CAN BE TOUGH. WRITE DOWN ONE OF YOUR FAVORITE QUOTES THAT REMINDS YOU WHY YOUR JOB IS SO IMPORTANT.

_____

_____

_____

_____

EXERCISE: CONSIDER THE SEVEN DEFINING CHARACTERISTICS OF GENERATION Z THAT DR. ELMORE OUTLINED IN THE CHAPTER. (PP. 60-63, *MARCHING OFF THE MAP*)

On the right, order each characteristic in it's probability to effect the classroom. A ranking of "1" means that this characteristic is the most important one for teachers and leaders of the next generation to consider.

REALISTIC   _____

PRIVATE   _____

ENTREPRENEURIAL   _____

MULTI-TASKING   _____

HYPER-AWARE   _____

OVERWHELMED   _____

TECHNOLOGY-RELIANT   _____

Why did you choose the order you did? Discuss this with a peer to compare your ideas and beliefs.

_____

_____

_____

_____

EXERCISE: ACCORDING TO THE GENERATIONAL CHART IN THE BOOK, WHAT GENERATION ARE YOU A PART OF? (PP. 64-65, *MARCHING OFF THE MAP*) OF THE PEOPLE WHO HAVE YOUR SAME POSITION ACROSS THE COUNTRY, HOW MANY WOULD YOU GUESS BELONG IN EACH GENERATION. DRAW A BAR GRAPH BELOW, REPRESENTING THE NUMBER OF PEERS YOU HAVE IN EACH GENERATION. (MAKE SURE YOUR BARS ADD UP TO 100 PERCENT)

	0%	25%	50%	75%	100%
BABY BOOMERS					
BABY BUSTERS (GEN X)					
MILLENNIALS (GEN Y)					

QUESTION: HOW IS THE GENERATIONAL DIVERSITY OF YOUR JOB (OR LACK OF) CHANGING YOUR PROFESSION? FOR INSTANCE, IF MANY OF YOUR PEERS ARE YOUNGER THAN YOU, IS THIS LEADING TO LOTS OF CHANGE?

_____

_____

_____

_____

QUESTION: HOW ARE YOU LEVERAGING WHAT YOU KNOW ABOUT THE NEXT GENERATION TO EQUIP THE YOUNG PEOPLE AROUND YOU FOR LIFE AFTER THE CLASSROOM? WRITE DOWN A SPECIFIC STORY THAT COMES TO MIND.

_____

_____

_____

_____

REFLECT AND RESPOND: CONSIDER THE THREE "BALANCING ACTS" THAT DR. ELMORE SUGGESTS FOR ALL LEADERS OF THE NEXT GENERATION (PP. 70-72, MARCHING OFF THE MAP). WE MUST BALANCE:

1. Being organized with being organic.

   Ask Yourself: The next time you plan an event or program for students, how could you involve them in the process to keep the program relevant? How could you insure the execution comes across simple, interactive and real?

   _____

   _____

   _____

   _____

2. Embracing the real and the ideal.

   Ask Yourself: When you communicate with your students, how can you relay that you are aware of the difficult realities they face (that your head is not in the sand)? But remember to relay the noble ideals you believe they are capable of growing into as adults. We must juggle the real and the ideal.

   _____

   _____

   _____

   _____

3. Celebrating both diversity and harmony.

   Ask Yourself: How can you communicate that you welcome the uniqueness of each student, while at the same time call them to work in collaboration and harmony toward a common goal?

_____

_____

_____

_____

Which of these balancing acts do you most need to pursue?

_____

_____

_____

_____

QUESTION: THINK ABOUT THE STUDENTS YOU WORK WITH REGULARLY. WHAT SOCIAL OR EMOTIONAL MUSCLES SEEM TO BE WEAK? WHAT PRACTICES CAN YOU INTRODUCE TO THEM TO DEVELOP THOSE MUSCLES? (PP. 74, *MARCHING OFF THE MAP*)

_____

_____

_____

_____

BONUS: SUPERFICIAL, SELF-ABSORBED, & SYNTHETIC

Superficial

USA Today recently carried an article called, "Looks Over Books." It detailed how college campus bookstores were making an exponential amount of income selling cosmetics over books to the students. Campus bookstore operator Barnes and Noble opened five of these beauty shops in 2015 and even more in 2016. Campus retailers believe it's recession proof too.

"When times get tough, shoppers still spend money to look glam," said journalist Hadley Malcolm. Wow. Beauty trumps books on campus.

In 2014, MSNBC interrupted a serious interview with congresswoman Jane Harman mid-sentence while talking about gun control… so they could report that Justin Bieber had been arrested on DUI charges. The news of Bieber's arrest had the entire media industry buzzing with producers eager to get their share of page views and eyes on the story. MSNBC isn't alone in this—CNN aired an hour-long special report titled "Bieber's Troubles" a show one might expect from 'Entertainment Tonight' or 'Access Hollywood', not 'The Most Trusted Name in News'.

Writer Ben Cohen acknowledged, "This is a seriously worrying feature of the news industry in America, and one that warrants a great deal of scrutiny. The long term effects of a major news network prioritizing news stories according to their virality is particularly toxic. Followed to its logical extreme, in a few years no one may be reporting on anything serious at all, and we'll be stuck in a nightmarish cocoon of listicles and cat stories. Just look at Buzzfeed—the prototype of the modern media company that exists solely to create viral content. Sure, it's hugely popular, but then so is Justin Bieber, and that doesn't make it any good."[1] The truth is, we're getting very good at sticking to the surface. Welcome to McCulture.

---

1. Cohen, Ben. "Andrea Mitchell Interrupts Congress Woman for Justin Bieber, Proves Irrelevance of Corporate Media." The Daily Banter. N.p., 24 Jan. 2014. Web. 12 June 2017.

Self-absorbed

We live in a time of self-expansion. Of personal platforms, narcissism, and selfies. Case in point. Right after their win over the San Francisco 49ers in a playoff game, Seattle cornerback Richard Sherman was so full of himself—he had to share some of it with us. In an interview, he boasted that he was the best cornerback in the NFL, dissing Michael Crabtree, the wide receiver he had covered. Sherman's agent, Jamie Fritz, told CNN Money that interest in his client had boomed since the remarks. Fritz believed millions in deals would be signed soon. Sherman is indeed, awesome. Just ask him. If the wide receiver he covered was so mediocre, however, as he said he was, why is he bragging? Wasn't he just doing his job? Whenever I see a player score, then celebrate his achievement so intensely that teammates can't even get close to him to share in his celebration, I marvel at his short-sighted perspective. If I'm not mistaken, ten other players helped him score, throwing a pass, making blocks and opening holes. It's about "we" not "I."

Earlier, I mentioned David Brook's discussion about an NPR program airing just after our World War II veterans returned from the war. He heard celebrities like Bing Crosby and others express their humble gratitude that the war was over. Yet, serving and sacrificing for their country was what people were supposed to do. They told us they were only doing their job. Following the program, David returned to his hotel and turned on the TV, just in time to see an NFL defensive player make a tackle. He was stunned at the ego and arrogance displayed as the athlete celebrated his work. He was so full of himself, teammates couldn't get near him to celebrate the "teamwork" required on the play. David Brooks said the contrast between the war veterans' humility and this player's ego was stunning. The vets had saved the free world. The athlete had stopped a three-yard run. But somehow, it's okay today to be full of oneself instead of saying, "I'm just doing my job." Welcome to McCulture.

Synthetic

If you watch news programs as I do, you might be aware of the fact that shallow or artificial stories are shared with the same seriousness as significant stories that shape our history. In other words, we are just as compelled with synthetic, artificial, and conjured up "news" (stories from Reality TV shows, celebrities, etc.) as we are with events that really matter. A network or cable news program will likely spend as much time talking about Kim Kardashian's weekend as it does on the economy or on poverty in America. The fact is, much of middle-class life isn't real: we are caught up in artificial concerns, synthetic ways to preoccupy our time and make us happy because we need coping mechanisms to endure our week. Welcome to McCulture.

Why did MSNBC interrupt an interview on gun control to talk about Justin Bieber? The answer is simple: we are superficial and synthetic. It's all about ratings, not informing the world on what's really important.

Why are arrogant athletes attracting new endorsement deals? Because we live in a time of self-expansion (and the expression of ego) after a game. But I think we forget at times that it is, indeed, just a game. I have a question for Richard Sherman: If Michael Crabtree is as "mediocre" as you said he is, why should you be bragging? If you only covered an average player, weren't you just doing your job?

Here's a thought. Let's decide to place life, sports and entertainment in perspective. Every athlete and actor should understand that even though people watch them do their job on a grand stage, they're still only doing a job. Most of us, however, will need to "add value" to our world, perhaps in a job that has no spotlight or microphone. That's where most of us live.

We all need to relocate...and move out of McCulture.

Ask your students: Do you see how superficial, self-absorbed, and synthetic our culture is today? How do we rise above it?

Chapter 5
WILL YOU SAIL OR SURRENDER?

A good sailor can take even contrary winds and use them. That's precisely what we must do.

- TIM ELMORE

REFLECT AND RESPOND: ONE STATISTIC DR. ELMORE UNCOVERED DURING THIS CHAPTER WAS THAT ONLY "2.7 PERCENT [OF TEACHERS SAY] THEY'D ENCOURAGE GRADUATES TO BECOME TEACHERS" (P. 80, *MARCHING OFF THE MAP*). WHAT ARE YOUR THOUGHTS ON THIS TREND? WHY DO SO MANY TEACHERS SEE THEIR PROFESSION AS A WASTE OF TIME OR A DEAD END?

_____

_____

_____

_____

REFLECT AND RESPOND: WHETHER YOU ARE A TEACHER, ADMINISTRATOR, OR ANOTHER KIND OF LEADER, CONSIDER YOUR THREE OPTIONS IN THE FACE OF DIFFICULTY:

1. Yell at the wind—Become angry, withdraw, complain, and just survive.

2. Surrender to the wind—Lose your resolve and give in to the culture's whims.

3. Adjust the sails—Use the current and wind to take students where they must go.

Which of these responses do you naturally lean toward? Why?
(p. 82, *Marching Off the Map*)

_____

_____

_____

_____

REFLECT AND RESPOND: CONSIDER THIS STATEMENT BY
DR. ELMORE:

"[Today's students] need adults to "adopt" what they were doing.
They need them to "adapt" to the current problems and respond
to them. They needed leaders, not imitators."

Think about your day-to-day job. What are some areas you can
"adapt" but not "adopt"? (p. 84, *Marching Off the Map*)

_____

_____

_____

_____

EXERCISE: REFERENCE PAGE 86 IN *MARCHING OFF THE MAP*.
ANSWER THE FOLLOWING QUESTIONS:

1. Are we moving in a good direction or an unhealthy one?

_____

_____

_____

_____

2. Can you think of any other shifts that have taken place?

_____

_____

_____

_____

3. How must we adapt to our day; to "adjust the sails," and still move forward, building timeless skills into our students?

_____

_____

_____

_____

EXERCISE: REVIEW THE "GAME CHANGERS" FOUND ON PAGES 88-91 IN *MARCHING OFF THE MAP*. CONSIDER HOW YOU MIGHT RESPOND TO THIS BIG QUESTION: WHICH OF THE "GAME CHANGERS" ABOVE ARE MOST RELEVANT TO YOU AND WHY?

_____

_____

_____

_____

EXERCISE: REFERENCE THE FOUR REALITIES ON PAGES 92-93 IN *MARCHING OFF THE MAP*. WHICH OF THE FOUR ITEMS ARE YOU EXPERIENCING?

☐ The recognition of an imminent threat

☐ The abandonment of an old practice

☐ The introduction of new technology

☐ The presence of rarely gifted leaders

EXERCISE: REFER TO THE "BIT MARKET" *HABITUDE®* REFERENCED ON PAGES 93-95 IN *MARCHING OFF THE MAP*. APPLY THE PRINCIPLE TO THE WORK YOU ARE DOING WITH STUDENTS, AND ANSWER THESE TWO QUESTIONS.

1. What is the "hole" you're trying to drill?

_____

_____

_____

_____

2. Is it time to trade out some old drill bits for new ones?

_____

_____

_____

_____

QUESTION: WHAT COULD YOU DO, THAT IF YOU DID IT, WOULD BE A GAME CHANGER FOR YOUR SCHOOL? (P. 96, *MARCHING OFF THE MAP*)

Chapter 6

THE SECRET TO HEALTHY PROGRESS:
SWING SETS AND PLUMB LINES

Our movement must lead to improvement.

- TIM ELMORE

EXERCISE: REVIEW THE SECTION IN *MARCHING OFF THE MAP* THAT TALKS ABOUT "SWING SETS" (PP. 102-103). ANSWER THE QUESTIONS BELOW ON BEHALF OF YOUR ORGANIZATION TO ILLUMINATE THE WAYS YOU NEED TO SWING BACKWARD AND SWING FORWARD. USE THE ANSWERS TO THESE QUESTIONS TO CREATE BEST PRACTICES FOR MAKING HEALTHY CHANGES.

Swinging Backward

What is our foundation and heritage?

_____

_____

Why did we decide to pursue our mission?

_____

_____

What value did we seek to add to our community?

_____

_____

What were the destructive elements we tried to discard?

_____

_____

Were there principles we felt are essential to sustain ourselves?

_____

_____

Swinging Forward
Where do we want to go today?

_____

_____

How is the landscape different than it was in the past?

_____

_____

What are the greatest needs we see in front of us?

_____

_____

What new methods or strategies do we need in the future?

_____

_____

How do we stay relevant by renewing our pledge to our mission?

_____

_____

QUESTION: NOW ASSEMBLE ALL OF YOUR THOUGHTS TOGETHER. HOW CAN WE USE THE PAST TO LEVERAGE THE FUTURE? WHAT ARE WAYS YOU CAN BALANCE YOUR TIMELESS PRINCIPLES WITH TODAY'S RELEVANT METHODS?

_____

_____

_____

_____

QUESTION: ON PAGE 107 IN *MARCHING OFF THE MAP*, DR. ELMORE WRITES, "SADLY, TOO MANY TEENS EXPERIENCE VIRTUAL MATURITY." THIS IS DUE, HE NOTES, "[TO THE FACT THAT] WE'VE SO CATEGORIZED CHILDHOOD. WE'RE AFRAID TO ALLOW THEM TO INTERFACE WITH REAL ISSUES AND CHALLENGES THAT WOULD ENGAGE THEIR HEARTS AND MINDS. SO NOW, WE SIMULATE THEM." WHAT ARE SOME SIMULATIONS OF THE REAL WORLD THAT YOUR KIDS OR STUDENTS REGULARLY ENGAGE IN? COMPARE YOUR LIST WITH A PEER.

_____

_____

_____

_____

QUESTION: THINK ABOUT THE FOLLOWING QUESTION FROM PAGE 109 IN *MARCHING OFF THE MAP*. WHAT IF WE AGREED UPON A PLUMB LINE AND HELD IT NEXT TO OUR HOMES, OUR SCHOOLS, OR OUR TEAMS? ARE WE CROOKED? ARE WE SHALLOW? HOW WOULD YOUR ORGANIZATION FARE?

_____

_____

_____

_____

QUESTION: REFER TO PAGE 109 IN *MARCHING OFF THE MAP* TO REVIEW THE "EIGHT ESSENTIAL LIFE SKILLS STUDENTS NEED". FOR EACH LIFE SKILL, EVALUATE YOURSELF ON HOW WELL YOU ARE HELPING TO BUILD THAT SKILL WITH YOUR STUDENTS. BE HONEST WITH YOURSELF.

How are you building problem-solving skills in your students?

A   B   C   D   F

How can you develop critical thinking skills in your students?

A   B   C   D   F

How are you cultivating emotional intelligence in your students?

A   B   C   D   F

How do you instill the practice of ethics and values in your students?

A   B   C   D   F

How do you incentivize resourcefulness and resilience in students?

A   B   C   D   F

How are you developing creative processing among your students?

A   B   C   D   F

How do you prepare students to practice analytic writing?

A   B   C   D   F

How are you equipping all of your students to think like leaders?

A   B   C   D   F

QUESTION: LOOK AT YOUR GRADE FOR ALL EIGHT LIFE SKILLS. FOCUS ON THE LIFE SKILLS YOU RATED THE LOWEST. DO YOU HAVE INTENTIONAL METHODS TO IMPART THESE LIFE SKILLS IN YOUR STUDENTS? WHAT CHANGES COULD YOU MAKE?

Chapter 7
How do We Lead Students from Apathy to Passion

We are far more engaged than our students.

- Tim Elmore

Question: Honestly evaluate yourself in the area of Metacognition. Do your students "own" their education? Why or why not? (p. 125, *Marching Off the Map*)

_____

_____

_____

_____

Exercise: How E.P.I.C. is your teaching style? For each component of the E.P.I.C. acronym, spend five minutes brainstorming ways you can utilize this component in your leadership with students. If you need help remembering the principle, refer to pages 125-130 in *Marching Off the Map.*

Experiential

Is there a way you could create a learning environment that uses experiences, not just instruction, to catalyze students to engage better? Even if it were once a week, what if you offered an experience and turned students loose to learn an idea by working experientially—and then discussing what they learned?

_____

_____

_____

_____

_____

_____

_____

Participatory

How could you provide a sense of "ownership" by allowing your students to weigh in on what or how they learned? How could you let them put their fingerprints on the subject so that it would look slightly different this year than last year, because they were in it? Is there any way they can personalize the ideas?

_____

_____

_____

_____

_____

_____

_____

Image Rich

How could you capitalize on an image or metaphor to relay the big idea you're attempting to communicate? While you must enable students to grasp rigorous and didactic concepts, how could you furnish a handle for them by using an icon to help them visualize and remember the idea?

_____

_____

_____

_____

_____

_____

Connected

How could you break down your larger class into smaller communities and allow them to connect with each other to solve a problem? When could you stop your lecture halfway through, and offer a well-crafted question to these small communities (a question that can't be answered with "yes" or "no.")?

_____

_____

_____

_____

_____

_____

REFLECT AND RESPOND: REVIEW THE "12 CONCLUSIONS I'VE DRAWN ABOUT LEARNING" SECTION ON PAGE 130 IN *MARCHING OF THE MAP*. WHICH OF THESE DO YOU EMBRACE AND PRACTICE? WHICH WOULD YOU LIKE TO START USING?

_____

_____

_____

_____

REFLECT AND RESPOND: REVIEW THE SECTION TITLED "SIMPLE IDEAS TO IGNITE METACOGNITION IN STUDENTS TODAY". WHICH OF THESE COULD YOU PUT INTO PRACTICE IMMEDIATELY WITH STUDENTS? (P. 134-135, *MARCHING OFF THE MAP*)

_____

_____

_____

_____

EXERCISE: REVIEW THE SIX LEVELS OF MOTIVATION IN STUDENTS ON PAGES 136-137 IN *MARCHING OFF THE MAP*. FOR EACH LEVEL, LIST OUT A FEW THINGS YOU DO TO MOTIVATE STUDENTS IN THIS WAY.

Six Levels of Motivation

1. I get to do something.

_____

_____

_____

_____

2. I get to do something interesting to me.

_____

_____

_____

_____

3. I get to do something interesting, using my gifts.

_____

_____

_____

_____

4. I get to do something interesting, using my gifts with people I enjoy.

_____

_____

_____

_____

5. I get to do something interesting, using my gifts with people I enjoy, and solve a problem.

_____

_____

_____

_____

6. I get to do something interesting, using my gifts with people I enjoy, solving a problem regarding something that matters.

_____

_____

_____

_____

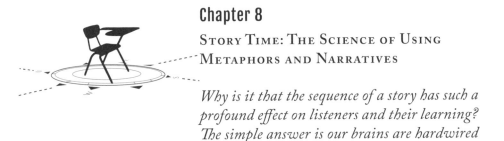

Chapter 8
Story Time: The Science of Using Metaphors and Narratives

Why is it that the sequence of a story has such a profound effect on listeners and their learning? The simple answer is our brains are hardwired this way.

− Tim Elmore

Exercise: Is your communication simple? Short? Sticky? Sharable? Rate yourself on each below. If you need a reminder, go to page 140 in *Marching Off the Map*.

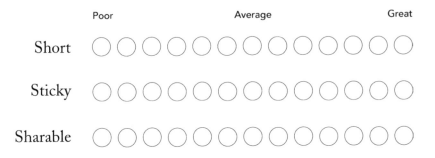

Poor   Average   Great

Short ○○○○○○○○○○○

Sticky ○○○○○○○○○○○

Sharable ○○○○○○○○○○○

Exercise: Think about an upcoming lesson you will be leading. Think of a story you can utilize to enable your learners to come up with the idea you want them to understand themselves, instead of merely suggesting the idea yourself. Outline your idea below.

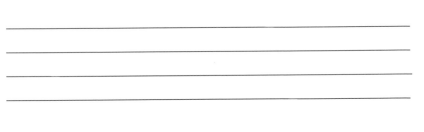

QUESTION: ANSWER THIS QUESTION AND THEN DISCUSS WITH A PEER OR CO-WORKER: HOW ARE YOU LEVERAGING THE POWER OF A STORY WHEN YOU COMMUNICATE? HAVE YOU MASTERED THE ART OF USING A STORY TO TEACH OR TRAIN? (P. 144, *MARCHING OFF THE MAP*)

_____

_____

_____

_____

QUESTION: REFER TO THE SECTION TITLED "PICTURE PERFECT COMMUNICATION" ON PAGES 147-157 IN *MARCHING OFF THE MAP*. WHAT OTHER REASONS WOULD YOU ADD TO THIS LIST? HOW DO YOU CAPITALIZE ON IMAGES WHEN YOU COMMUNICATE?

_____

_____

_____

_____

EXERCISE: THINK ABOUT THE RIGHT-BRAINED ACTIVITIES VERSUS THE LEFT-BRAINED ACTIVITIES THAT YOU DO EACH DAY WITH YOUR STUDENTS. MAKE A LIST FOR EACH. WHICH ONE IS LONGER? WHAT COULD YOU DO TO BETTER BALANCE OPPORTUNITIES FOR BOTH SIDES OF THE BRAIN? (P. 153, *MARCHING OFF THE MAP*)

Left-Brained Activities	Right-Brained Activities

Reflect and Respond: Where could you try rolling the "DICE" in your teaching? Take one of your lessons plans and quickly outline what it would look like to teach that same lesson using the "DICE" methodology. Try it out during your next lesson! (pp. 154, *Marching Off the Map*)

_____

_____

_____

_____

Chapter 9

MODERN DAY MAP MAKERS

The reality of a vision for the future is that only a few people see it, and even fewer are willing to take the risks associated with change.

- ANDREW MCPEAK

QUESTION: WHAT MOMENT IN YOUR LIFE WOULD YOU POINT TO AS THE GENESIS OF THE PURPOSE AND ASPIRATION OF YOUR WORK? WHEN DID YOU FIRST DISCOVER YOUR PASSION? (P. 163, *MARCHING OFF THE MAP*)

_____

_____

_____

_____

QUESTION: WHAT WAS YOUR VISION WHEN YOU STARTED YOUR WORK AS AN EDUCATOR? WHAT DIFFERENCE DID YOU WANT TO MAKE IN THE WORLD? (P. 163, *MARCHING OFF THE MAP*)

_____

_____

_____

_____

QUESTION: THINK ABOUT YOUR ANSWERS TO THE TWO QUESTIONS ABOVE. HOW WILL YOU TURN YOUR GREATEST VISIONS OF THE FUTURE INTO PRACTICAL DAY-IN AND DAY-OUT PLANS? WHAT ARE SIMPLE ACTIONS THAT CAN HELP YOU ACCOMPLISH THESE LOFTY GOALS? (P. 164, *MARCHING OFF THE MAP*)

_____

_____

_____

_____

QUESTION: ANSWER HONESTLY: ARE YOU WILLING TO DO WHATEVER IT TAKES TO ACHIEVE YOUR MISSION? IS THERE SOMETHING HOLDING YOU BACK? (P. 165, *MARCHING OFF THE MAP*)

_____

_____

_____

_____

QUESTION: REFER BACK TO THE STORIES OF "MODERN-DAY MAP MAKERS" IN CHAPTER NINE. WHICH STORY WAS MOST INSPIRATIONAL? WHICH OF THESE CASE STUDIES COULD YOU UTILIZE TO BEST TRANSFORM YOUR WORK? (P. 172, *MARCHING OFF THE MAP*)

_____

_____

_____

_____

QUESTION: NOW, TELL YOUR OWN STORY. WHO IS ONE PERSON YOU KNOW OF WHO INSPIRES YOU IN YOUR WORK? WHAT MAKES THEM A MODERN-DAY MAP MAKER?

Chapter 10

STORMS ON THE HORIZON

Anyone who marches off the map should expect to encounter some turbulent weather.

- TIM ELMORE

EXERCISE: SOCIAL MEDIA IS A FORCE FOR GOOD AND A FORCE FOR DAMAGE IN OUR YOUTH. ANSWER THE FOLLOWING QUESTIONS TO EVALUATE THE ISSUES RELATED TO SOCIAL MEDIA FOR YOUR STUDENTS (P. 185, MARCHING OFF THE MAP):

1. What symptoms have you observed when students use social media?

2. What could you do to convince them to use social media in moderation?

3. What are you doing to leverage social media for
constructive purposes?

_____

_____

_____

_____

REFLECT AND RESPOND: WRITE DOWN SOME THOUGHTS TO
ANSWER THIS QUESTION AND THEN DISCUSS IT WITH A PEER OR
CO-WORKER: HOW CAN WE BALANCE OUR STUDENT'S TIME ON
SOCIAL MEDIA WITH FACE-TO-FACE INTERACTION? HOW CAN WE
ENSURE THEY BECOME EMOTIONALLY HEALTHY ADULTS? (P. 187,
MARCHING OFF THE MAP)

_____

_____

_____

_____

EXERCISE: CAN YOU LIST SOME EXAMPLES OF BOTH RELATIVE
MORALS AND TIMELESS MORALS IN OUR CULTURE? REFER TO
PAGE 191 IN MARCHING OFF THE MAP TO REMIND YOURSELF OF
THE DIFFERENCE.

Relative Morals:

_____

_____

_____

_____

Timeless Morals:

_____

_____

_____

_____

QUESTION: HAVE YOU CLEARLY COMMUNICATED THE DIFFERENCE BETWEEN RELATIVE AND TIMELESS TO YOUR STUDENTS? WHAT ARE SOME WAYS THAT YOU COULD EXPLAIN IT TO THEM? (HINT: THINK E.P.I.C.!)

_____

_____

_____

_____

QUESTION: REVIEW THE SECTION TITLED "THE POTENTIAL UPSIDE" ON PAGE 194 IN THE _MARCHING OFF THE MAP_. IN WHAT WAYS CAN WE CAPITALIZE ON THESE POSITIVE REALITIES?

_____

_____

_____

Exercise: In the chapter, Dr. Elmore mentions several social technologies you can use in the classroom. What technologies are you currently using to increase student social engagement? List them here. (p. 195-196, *Marching Off the Map*)

_____

_____

_____

_____

_____

_____

_____

Bonus: The ABC's of Guiding Students on Social Media

My question for you is simple: Are you OK with the impacts social media is having on our young? Do you believe we have any responsibility to guide them with their social media consumption? With their social habits? Within the set of ethics they embrace? Can we be intentional about mentoring students as they grow up with unlimited access to content and perhaps no consequence to their posts? How do we appropriately lead our students in this kind of day? Certainly, there's an upside and a downside to social media. While it may evolve over time, it's obviously not going away. So, how do we help them manage their time and attention? Let me suggest three principles that can guide us.

A—Awareness

As caring adults, we've got to be more aware of the reality they're experiencing. Teens told us (in our focus groups) that both parents and teachers have no idea what they're up to in a day of vanishing messages and multiple screens. Take their phone away, and they've got a tablet to get online. In 1995, teens spent 2.5 hours daily on digital media, and it was a Walkman. In 2005, teens spent 6 hours on digital media and it was an MP3 player (iPod). In 2015, it's now the equivalent of a full-time job (9.0 hours) on a screen and it's primarily social media.[1] Do you know what they consume during those hours? Can you guide them in making good decisions on their consumption of it, whether its determining credible sources of data or deciding not to "meet in real life" with that person they met online? Become aware, and let them know you're aware of the sites they spend their time on.

B—Balance

Talk to them about the idea of balance. It's a much-used word today, but rarely practiced. We're "binge-consumers" of media—Netflix, Twitter, and Facebook, you name it. I believe this is part of the teen mental health problem today. We've given up on the idea of moderation. We have a tough time with self-regulation. (Adults do too). So, when you see your students indulging in social media, find a time (later) to talk about it. Affirm the fact that you're glad they're so adept with technology; after all, they'll likely use it in their career. But share the research behind too much digital consumption and how it can negatively impact the development of their

---

1. "The Digital Diet of the American Teen [Infographic]." Rawhide. N.p., 07 Apr. 2017. Web. 04 June 2017.

emotional intelligence, employability skills (socially), and the ability to delay gratification. (Note: Steve Jobs wouldn't allow his own kids to have an iPad, the device he himself built!)Help them to self-regulate. In other words, suggest they set a timer on their phone when they go online and stop when that timer goes off.

C—Change

Once they see the need to moderate their time on a screen, help them to change their habits. Offer some ideas on how they can substitute that previous screen time for face-to-face time with friends, participation on a team, or connect with friends on projects to serve the community. The key is trading off the time they'd spend on social media for something just as engaging but also constructive or redemptive. This is a sign of maturity: the ability to discipline yourself to overcome addictive behaviors by exchanging that unhealthy habit for a healthy one. Moderation can help prevent addiction. Self-regulation is a sign of maturity and adulthood. Like you, I discovered long ago that the best way to end a bad habit is to replace it with a good one.

Chapter 11

Trouble Back Home

Every move we make impacts others. Every decision affects others. Every conversation influences others.

- Tim Elmore

QUESTION: REVIEW THE SECTION TITLED "IMPROVING YOURSELF, BUILDING NEW HABITS AND ATTITUDES AS YOU LEAD" ON PAGE 201 IN *MARCHING OFF THE MAP*. WHAT CHANGE DO YOU WANT TO PERSONALLY MAKE? WHEN WILL YOU START? WOULD ANY OF THESE STEPS BE RELEVANT?

_____

_____

_____

_____

QUESTION: REVIEW THE METHODS FOR INFLUENCING AUTHORITIES ON PAGE 202 IN *MARCHING OFF THE MAP*. WHICH OF THESE STEPS ARE DOABLE FOR YOU? WHICH WILL BE DIFFICULT?

_____

_____

_____

_____

EXERCISE: REVIEW THE SECTION TITLED "THE DAY I STOPPED ASKING THE WRONG QUESTIONS" ON PAGE 210 IN *MARCHING OFF THE MAP*. IN PARTICULAR, CONSIDER THE LIST OF QUESTIONS ON PAGE 211. THINK ABOUT THE QUESTIONS YOU ASK YOUR STUDENTS ON A TYPICAL DAY. WHAT QUESTIONS DO YOU NEED TO STOP ASKING? WHAT QUESTIONS SHOULD YOU START ASKING? MAKE A LIST BELOW.

Questions I need to stop asking	Questions I need to start asking

QUESTION: HOW COULD START TO REFRAME THE QUESTIONS YOU ASK STUDENTS? (P. 212, *MARCHING OFF THE MAP*)

_____

_____

_____

_____

Chapter 12

A Most Important Final Word

In a challenging situation, we must lead out of belief in the potential of the student. We pull out the best in them when we believe the best about them.

- Tim Elmore

QUESTION: In your experience, what are some of the differences between leaders and teachers who communicate out of relief rather than those who communicate out of belief? What impact does it have on the students? (p. 216, *Marching Off the Map*)

_____

_____

_____

_____

EXERCISE: Evaluate how well you are both responsive and demanding (p. 217, *Marching Off the Map*). List out the actions that you do on a typical day that are responsive and the ones that are demanding. Is there a balance of both? Do you naturally lean toward one side or the other?

Responsive	Demanding

QUESTION: CAN YOU THINK OF A TIME WHEN A LEADER COMMUNICATED BELIEF IN YOU? WHY DO YOU THINK THIS MOMENT WAS SO MEMORABLE FOR YOU? (P. 218, *MARCHING OFF THE MAP*)

_____

_____

_____

_____

QUESTION: REVIEW THE SECTION TITLED "TAKING THE PATH OF BELIEF" ON PAGE 223 IN *MARCHING OFF THE MAP*. WHICH OF THE ACTIONS ON THIS LIST COULD YOU START USING IN YOUR WORK WITH STUDENTS THIS WEEK?

_____

_____

_____

_____

Epilogue

THREE STRATEGIC SOLUTIONS

If we will get these three areas right, they'll perform better in the classroom, on the ballfield, in the work place and at home

- TIM ELMORE

QUESTION: HOW ARE YOU HELPING STUDENTS INTEGRATE THEIR LIVES AND PRACTICE MINDFULNESS? WHAT ARE SOME PRACTICES YOU COULD USE ON THE LIST FROM PAGES 229-230 TO HELP YOU LEAD THEM WELL? (P. 231, *MARCHING OFF THE MAP*)

_____

_____

_____

_____

QUESTION: WHAT CAN WE LEARN FROM EVEN UNHEALTHY MOVEMENTS OR ORGANIZATIONS AROUND US ABOUT REACHING KIDS? ARE WE INSPIRING GENERATION Z AS WELL? WHAT KEEPS US FROM BEING INSPIRING IN THE CLASSROOM? (P. 235, *MARCHING OFF THE MAP*)

_____

_____

_____

_____

QUESTION: How could you inspire hope and vision within the students you lead? (p. 236, *Marching Off the Map*)

_____

_____

_____

_____

QUESTION: Consider the "Four Components to a Healthy Identity" on page 239 in *Marching Off the Map*. Which of these areas are your students lacking the most? How could you help them better build their identity?

_____

_____

_____

_____

Thank you for taking this journey through your travel guide. We hope that you were able to evaluate your leadership well as you read through the content in *Marching Off the Map*. We encourage you to share your thoughts with others, start discussion groups, and return to this guide in the future to re-evaluate your leadership. Also, be sure to check out the *Marching Off the Map* website for additional resources at:

marchingoffthemap.com

NOTES

NOTES

NOTES